JAZZ
ALTO SAX
LEVEL/GRADE 3
TUNES

ABRSM

Published by ABRSM (Publishing) Ltd, a wholly owned subsidiary of ABRSM, 24 Portland Place, London W1B 1LU, United Kingdom

Reprinted in 2005, 2006, 2008, 2010, 2012

ISBN 978 1 86096 306 3
AB 2864

Lead Jazz Consultant: Charles Beale
Sax Consultants: Iain Dixon, Mike Hall, Martin Hathaway, Andy Panayi, Tony Woods
Consultant Jazz Editors: Pete Churchill, Nikki Iles
Project Editor: Hywel Davies

Special thanks are also due to the following for their help in developing the repertoire for this project:
John Barton, Mark Bassey, Chris Batchelor, Dave Bitelli, Jim Clarke, Dave Cliff, Alan Cohen, Ralf Dorrell, Digby Fairweather, Sid Gauld, Frank Griffith, Stuart Hall, Eddie Harvey, Paul Jayasinha, Mike Mower, Keith Nichols, Mark Nightingale, Gerard Presencer, Brian Priestley, Simon Purcell, Geoff Simkins, Stan Sulzmann, Ray Warleigh, Huw Warren, Steve Waterman, Annie Whitehead

Music setting by Barnes Music Engraving Ltd, East Sussex

designed by ●●● 9thplanet

Printed in England by Caligraving Ltd, Thetford, Norfolk

MIX
Paper from responsible sources
FSC
www.fsc.org   FSC™ C109619

CONTENTS

INTRODUCTION   5

Blues & Roots

JOHN COLTRANE arr. Liam Noble
Blue Train   7

SONNY ROLLINS arr. Pete Whittaker
Playing in the Yard   8

MILES DAVIS arr. Nikki Iles
All Blues   9

EDDIE HARRIS arr. Iain Dixon
Cold Duck Time   10

HORACE SILVER arr. Liam Noble
The Preacher   11

Standards

JOE ZAWINUL arr. Phil Peskett
Mercy, Mercy, Mercy   12

THOMAS 'FATS' WALLER & ANDY RAZAF
arr. Nick Tomalin
Honeysuckle Rose   13

VINCENT YOUMANS & IRVING CAESAR
arr. Bill Kinghorn
Tea for Two   14

JOSEPH KOSMA & JOHNNY MERCER arr. Nikki Iles
Autumn Leaves   15

GEORGE & IRA GERSHWIN arr. Nikki Iles
Lady Be Good   16

Contemporary Jazz

TIM GARLAND
Sister Moon   17

MARK LOCKHEART arr. Pete Churchill
Going Home   18

DON CHERRY arr. Huw Warren
Mopti   19

Notice
ABRSM has reluctantly removed this piece from this book.
Despite many efforts, we have been unable to obtain permission
from the copyright owner to reproduce it for reprint.

TIM WHITEHEAD
All Is Well   20

MIKE MAINIERI arr. Mike Hall
Sara's Touch   21

PLAYING THE TUNES IN AN EXAM   22

CD TRACK LISTING   24

JAZZ ALTO SAX
LEVEL/GRADE 3
INTRODUCTION

Welcome to this book of jazz tunes, arranged for alto sax Level/Grade 3, which forms part of the ABRSM Jazz Syllabus. The tunes cover a wide range of styles – from New Orleans and swing through to jazz-rock and Brazilian bossa – and are divided into three lists: Blues & Roots, Standards and Contemporary Jazz.

In each category there are five tunes. Each arrangement contains a fully notated HEAD, the main melody; an indication of the feel, that is straight 8s or swing; and a tempo indication (a metronome mark) representing the **minimum** exam speed for the tune at this Level/Grade. Every tune has at least one section for improvisation, marked SOLOS, with a simple chord sequence and set of guideline pitches. These pitches – appearing in boxes and shown as black noteheads without tails – give a suggested starting point to help you begin soloing. As you become more familiar with the material, you should experiment with using other pitches.

Blues & Roots draws from all periods of jazz and contains tunes based on the 12-bar blues or blues of other lengths. The list also includes African-American spirituals, other musics of New Orleans, and roots tunes from other continents. The tunes and chord sequences (or 'changes') in this list are mostly groove-based and are relatively straightforward.

Standards, as the term suggests, contains core repertoire of the jazz tradition. This includes familiar Tin Pan Alley and Broadway tunes, arranged in the rhythmic and harmonic styles of jazz, and more recent standards from swing, bebop, hard bop and other established styles. Some arrangements reproduce important past performances, while others give new perspectives on familiar tunes. Occasionally, lesser-known tunes by important performers or composers are also included. In this list, chord sequences and structures often incorporate AABA forms and II-V-I progressions.

Contemporary Jazz represents the vibrancy, eclecticism and even the fragmentation of jazz since the early 1970s. There are fusion pieces and overlaps with related styles, including rock and folk musics from around the world, plus contemporary tunes from South Africa, Europe and the American continent. Some tunes from this list were specially commissioned by ABRSM.

JAZZ ALTO SAX
LEVEL/GRADE 3
INTRODUCTION

Jazz is an aural tradition; the best way to learn is to listen to live or recorded performances. It is always good to hear how other performers have interpreted tunes you are working on, or to listen to tunes that are similar in style. With this in mind, each arrangement carries at least one Related Listening suggestion: a track, its album and record label. The availability of the listed albums has been checked as thoroughly as possible, but jazz recordings continually go in and out of issue. If you have difficulty finding them, try your local library (which usually has access to other libraries), the Internet or a specialist jazz-record supplier. In place of a specific label, 'various' indicates that the artist recorded this tune on a number of albums (including compilations) and that any of these recordings is considered suitable.

Additionally, for each arrangement, there is a footnote on the tune's history or style, its composer(s) or key performers, and, where relevant, technical advice from a jazz saxophonist. We hope that these insights provide fresh ideas and will help you develop a sense of style.

The CD at the back of this book contains a recording of each arrangement and a 'minus-one' version of the track for you to play along with. The minus-one tracks can be used in ABRSM jazz exams (we accept, however, that live accompaniment – whether small band or piano, guitar etc. – is truer to the spirit of jazz). The recorded arrangement reflects the exam routine; please note the number of bars required for the exam solo. Outside the exam – while practising or in non-exam performances – you can extend solos by repeating all or part of the SOLOS section.

At Levels/Grades 1–3 some of the tunes are arranged in keys other than the original, so that they are playable by less experienced musicians. By Level/Grade 4, however, all tunes are in their most regularly performed keys.

Jazz exams offer a great way to measure your progress, to give your work an added focus and to enable you to achieve your potential. ABRSM's graded exams are based on what an average student achieves during the course of one year, so that Level/Grade 5, for example, represents five years' work. At every level, candidates for these exams are assessed by musicians with broad jazz experience. For more information, please read 'Playing the Tunes in an Exam' at the back of this book.

We hope you enjoy playing these tunes as much as we have enjoyed selecting, arranging and recording them.

BLUE TRAIN

JOHN COLTRANE
arr. Liam Noble

John Coltrane (1926–67) took tenor sax playing to new heights of emotional intensity and technical skill. This Coltrane blues has a 'call and response' form. Those familiar with Miles Davis's 'So What' will recognize the 'response'.
RELATED LISTENING John Coltrane: Title track from *Blue Train* (Blue Note)

PLAYING IN THE YARD
SONNY ROLLINS
arr. Pete Whittaker

New Orleans-style straight 8s ♩ = 124 **Bright and playful**

This Sonny Rollins tune has a New Orleans feel thanks to the rhythmic ostinato of the accompaniment. Like many of Rollins's best tunes, 'Playing in the Yard' is short, simple and catchy, but still allows plenty of scope for varying your improvisation.
RELATED LISTENING Sonny Rollins: 'Playing in the Yard' from *Next Album* (Original Jazz Classics)

ALL BLUES

MILES DAVIS
arr. Nikki Iles

In the liner notes to the album *Kind of Blue* (1959) this tune was described as a '6/8 12-measure blues form'. On the same recording, which this arrangement is based on, the mood is restrained and the dynamic changes are subtle. To extend solos, play the 12-bar blues form for bars 3–14. Play the sixteenth-notes (semiquavers) as you would eighth-notes (quavers) in a swing tune.

RELATED LISTENING Miles Davis: 'All Blues' from *Kind of Blue* (Columbia/Sony)

COLD DUCK TIME

EDDIE HARRIS
arr. Iain Dixon

Eddie Harris started his career as a bop player, but went on to play with rock and soul-jazz bands in the late 1960s. This earthy tune tends to combine these styles in its use of #9 chords, a spiky straight-8s funk rhythm and the Bb7 chord in the head. Try using the rhythm of the tune to extend and develop your solo.
RELATED LISTENING Eddie Harris and Les McCann: 'Cold Duck Time' from *Swiss Movement* (Atlantic)

THE PREACHER

HORACE SILVER
arr. Liam Noble

Horace Silver's 1954 recording of this tune is one of the earliest examples of hard bop, a style of jazz after bebop that returned to rhythm-and-blues and gospel music. Don't be afraid to 'play the blues' here.

RELATED LISTENING Horace Silver: 'The Preacher' from *Horace Silver and the Jazz Messengers* (Blue Note) and *Horace Silver, The Story of Jazz* (EMI Jazz)

MERCY, MERCY, MERCY

JOE ZAWINUL
arr. Phil Peskett

Joe Zawinul (1932–2007) worked with Cannonball Adderley and Miles Davis before forming his groundbreaking jazz-rock band Weather Report, in 1971. In later work, Zawinul used synthesizers, samplers and other technology in jazz and improvised music. This tune is written in a gospel style.

RELATED LISTENING Cannonball Adderley: 'Mercy, Mercy, Mercy' from *Mercy, Mercy, Mercy!* (Capitol) and *The Definitive Cannonball Adderley* (Blue Note)

HONEYSUCKLE ROSE

THOMAS 'FATS' WALLER & ANDY RAZAF
arr. Nick Tomalin

Fats Waller (1904–43) was a great player of stride piano (a solo piano style and form of ragtime). Working in the 1920s and 30s as a singer and entertainer, Fats wrote several songs that were to become popular jazz standards. 'Honeysuckle Rose' is a favourite of many musicians; its chord sequence has re-emerged as the basis for several bebop compositions, for example.
RELATED LISTENING Benny Carter: 'Honeysuckle Rose' from *Further Definitions* (Impulse!)

Music by Thomas 'Fats' Waller Lyrics by Andy Razaf
© 1929 Chappell & Co Inc, USA. Redwood Music Ltd, London NW1 8BD (for British Reversionary Territories) and Warner/Chappell North America Ltd, London W6 8BS (for World excl. British Reversionary Territories). Reproduced by permission of Faber Music Ltd. All Rights Reserved.

TEA FOR TWO

VINCENT YOUMANS & IRVING CAESAR
arr. Bill Kinghorn

All jazz musicians have played this hoary old standard at some point, and yet it still continues to charm. The chord sequence of the tune is unusual because the second eight bars of the head are the first eight transposed up a major 3rd. At the end of phrases, try filling in the spaces with your own lines.

RELATED LISTENING Bud Powell: 'Tea for Two' from *The Genius of Bud Powell* (Verve) and *The Definitive Bud Powell* (Blue Note)

14

CONTENTS

JAZZ
ALTO SAX
LEVEL/GRADE 3
TUNES
PIANO ACCOMPANIMENT

Blues & Roots

JOHN COLTRANE arr. Liam Noble
Blue Train   2

SONNY ROLLINS arr. Pete Whittaker
Playing in the Yard   5

MILES DAVIS arr. Nikki Iles
All Blues   8

EDDIE HARRIS arr. Iain Dixon
Cold Duck Time   11

HORACE SILVER arr. Liam Noble
The Preacher   14

Standards

JOE ZAWINUL arr. Phil Peskett
Mercy, Mercy, Mercy   17

THOMAS 'FATS' WALLER & ANDY RAZAF
arr. Nick Tomalin
Honeysuckle Rose   20

VINCENT YOUMANS & IRVING CAESAR
arr. Bill Kinghorn
Tea for Two   24

JOSEPH KOSMA & JOHNNY MERCER arr. Nikki Iles
Autumn Leaves   28

GEORGE & IRA GERSHWIN arr. Nikki Iles
Lady Be Good   32

Contemporary Jazz

TIM GARLAND
Sister Moon   35

MARK LOCKHEART arr. Pete Churchill
Going Home   38

DON CHERRY arr. Huw Warren
Mopti   41

Notice
ABRSM has reluctantly removed this piece from this book.
Despite many efforts, we have been unable to obtain permission
from the copyright owner to reproduce it for reprint.

TIM WHITEHEAD
All Is Well   44

MIKE MAINIERI arr. Mike Hall
Sara's Touch   46

ABRSM

BLUE TRAIN
JOHN COLTRANE
arr. Liam Noble

Relaxed swing ♩ = 115 | HEAD

SOLO BREAK

John Coltrane (1926–67) took tenor sax playing to new heights of emotional intensity and technical skill. This Coltrane blues has a 'call and response' form. Those familiar with Miles Davis's 'So What' will recognize the 'response'.
RELATED LISTENING John Coltrane: Title track from *Blue Train* (Blue Note)

PLAYING IN THE YARD

SONNY ROLLINS
arr. Pete Whittaker

> This Sonny Rollins tune has a New Orleans feel thanks to the rhythmic ostinato of the accompaniment. Like many of Rollins's best tunes, 'Playing in the Yard' is short, simple and catchy, but still allows plenty of scope for varying your improvisation.
> **RELATED LISTENING** Sonny Rollins: 'Playing in the Yard' from *Next Album* (Original Jazz Classics)

SOLOS

ALL BLUES

MILES DAVIS
arr. Nikki Iles

In the liner notes to the album *Kind of Blue* (1959) this tune was described as a '6/8 12-measure blues form'. On the same recording, which this arrangement is based on, the mood is restrained and the dynamic changes are subtle. The right-hand figure (if played) in the accompaniment at bars 1–2 should be a quiet murmur. To extend solos, play the 12-bar blues form for bars 3–14. Play the sixteenth-notes (semiquavers) as you would eighth-notes (quavers) in a swing tune.

RELATED LISTENING Miles Davis: 'All Blues' from *Kind of Blue* (Columbia/Sony)

COLD DUCK TIME

EDDIE HARRIS
arr. Iain Dixon

Straight 8s funk ♩ = 144

Eddie Harris started his career as a bop player, but went on to play with rock and soul-jazz bands in the late 1960s. This earthy tune tends to combine these styles in its use of #9 chords, a spiky straight-8s funk rhythm and the Db7 chord in the head.
RELATED LISTENING Eddie Harris and Les McCann: 'Cold Duck Time' from *Swiss Movement* (Atlantic)

Solo 16 bars in exam

HEAD continues

D.S. al Coda

⊕ **CODA**

THE PREACHER

HORACE SILVER
arr. Liam Noble

Horace Silver's 1954 recording of this tune is one of the earliest examples of hard bop, a style of jazz after bebop that returned to rhythm-and-blues and gospel music.

RELATED LISTENING Horace Silver: 'The Preacher' from *Horace Silver and the Jazz Messengers* (Blue Note) and *Horace Silver, The Story of Jazz* (EMI Jazz)

MERCY, MERCY, MERCY

JOE ZAWINUL
arr. Phil Peskett

Straight 8s ♩ = 100 **Soulful**

Joe Zawinul (1932–2007) worked with Cannonball Adderley and Miles Davis before forming his groundbreaking jazz-rock band Weather Report, in 1971. In later work, Zawinul used synthesizers, samplers and other technology in jazz and improvised music. This tune is written in a gospel style.

RELATED LISTENING Cannonball Adderley: 'Mercy, Mercy, Mercy' from *Mercy, Mercy, Mercy!* (Capitol) and *The Definitive Cannonball Adderley* (Blue Note)

19

HONEYSUCKLE ROSE

THOMAS 'FATS' WALLER & ANDY RAZAF
arr. Nick Tomalin

Medium swing ♩ = 124 **Stride style**

Fats Waller (1904–43) was a great player of stride piano (a solo piano style and form of ragtime). Working in the 1920s and 30s as a singer and entertainer, Fats wrote several songs that were to become popular jazz standards. 'Honeysuckle Rose' is a favourite of many musicians; its chord sequence has re-emerged as the basis for several bebop compositions, for example.
RELATED LISTENING Benny Carter: 'Honeysuckle Rose' from *Further Definitions* (Impulse!)

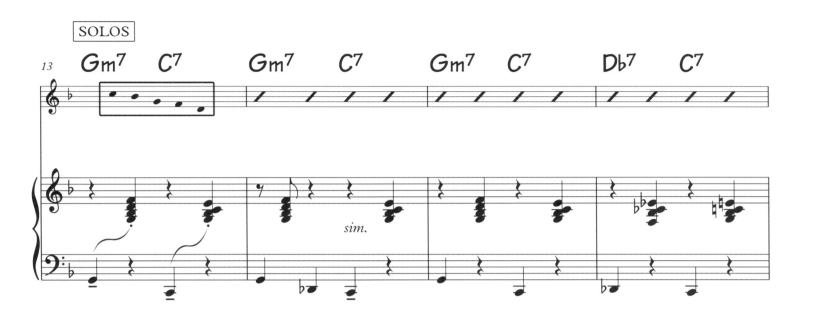

HEAD continues

TEA FOR TWO

VINCENT YOUMANS & IRVING CAESAR
arr. Bill Kinghorn

All jazz musicians have played this hoary old standard at some point, and yet it still continues to charm. The chord sequence of the tune is unusual because the second eight bars of the head are the first eight transposed up a major 3rd.
RELATED LISTENING Bud Powell: 'Tea for Two' from *The Genius of Bud Powell* (Verve) and *The Definitive Bud Powell* (Blue Note)

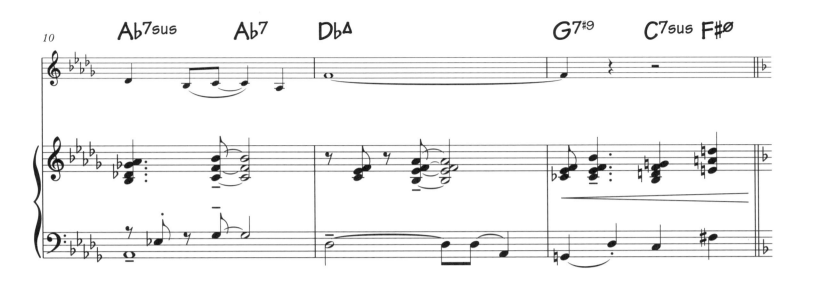

Livelier

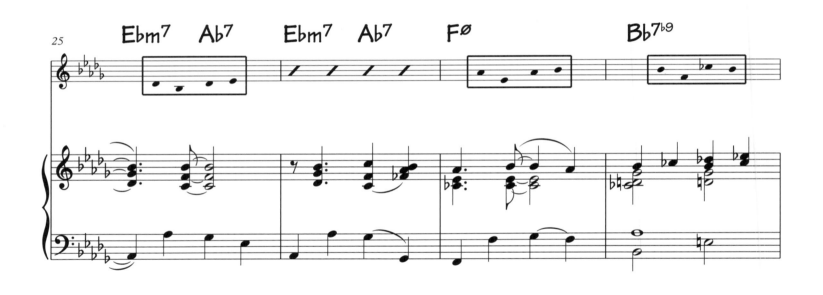

Straight 8s. Freely and whimsically

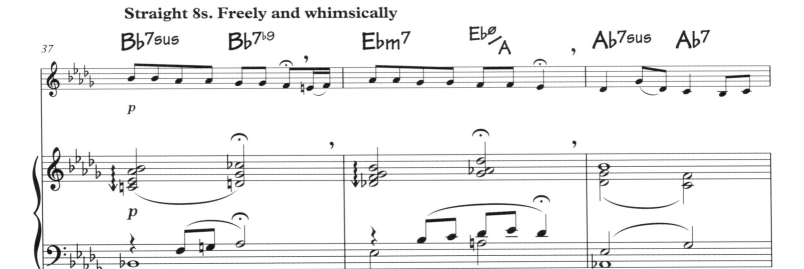

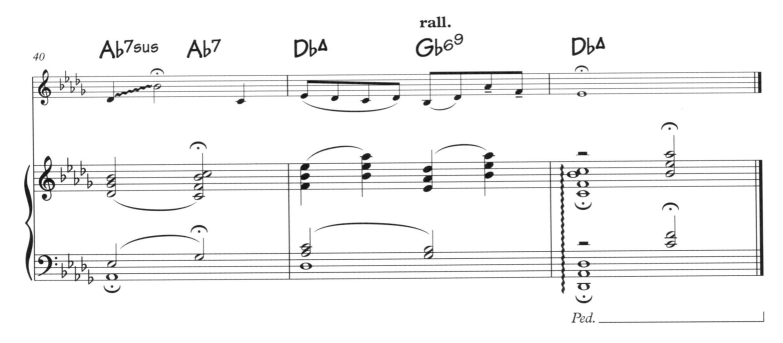

AUTUMN LEAVES

JOSEPH KOSMA & JOHNNY MERCER
arr. Nikki Iles

The essential jazz standard, 'Autumn Leaves' is to be found on page one of many jazz textbooks – it works well in a range of styles and has been interpreted by all the great improvisers, from Django Reinhardt to Miles Davis. Its chord sequence is based around two key centres: G minor (in concert pitch) and its relative major, Bb. The arrangement here reflects Bill Evans's interpretation rather than Cannonball's.

RELATED LISTENING Cannonball Adderley: 'Autumn Leaves' from *Somethin' Else* (Blue Note)
Bill Evans: 'Autumn Leaves' from *Portrait in Jazz* (Original Jazz Classics)

Music by Joseph Kosma   Lyrics by Johnny Mercer (after J. Prévert)

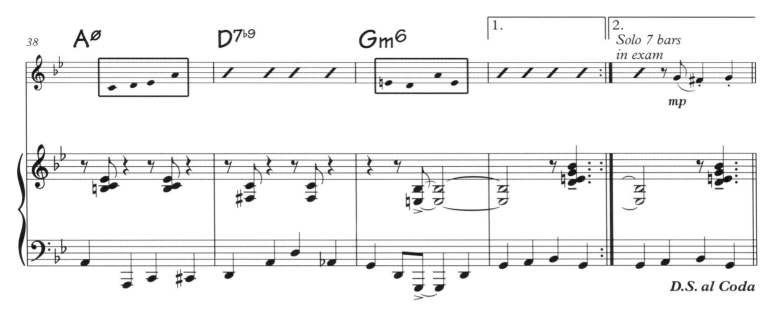

D.S. al Coda

LADY BE GOOD

GEORGE & IRA GERSHWIN
arr. Nikki Iles

George Gershwin (1898–1937) was a celebrated American songwriter, pianist and composer of concert music (including the famous *Rhapsody in Blue*). The true title of this song is in fact 'Oh, Lady, Be Good!', but this is normally shortened, as above. The song became the setting for a very famous sax solo recorded by Lester Young, in 1936.

RELATED LISTENING 'Lady Be Good' from *Jazz at the Philharmonic* (Arpeggio)
Lester Young: Title track from *Lady Be Good* (BCD)
Ella Fitzgerald: Title track from *Oh, Lady, Be Good!* (Verve)

SISTER MOON
TIM GARLAND

Composed by English saxophonist Tim Garland (b. 1966), 'Sister Moon' is lyrical and nocturnal, but it is not a ballad. Nor is it strictly speaking a bossa nova, despite the steady offbeats and the rhythm of the accompaniment. The rhythm found here is typical of some Brazilian music, particularly that of Egberto Gismonti.

RELATED LISTENING Tim Garland: 'The Moon for Her' from *Made by Walking* (Stretch)

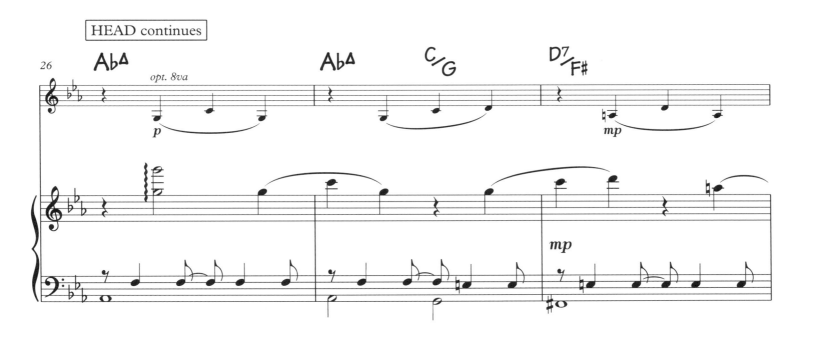

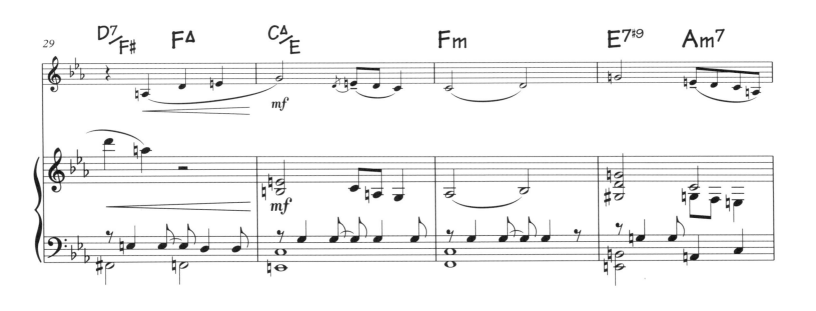

GOING HOME

MARK LOCKHEART
arr. Pete Churchill

Straight 8s ballad ♩ = 88 **Expressively**

Saxophonist Mark Lockheart (b. 1961) plays in Perfect Houseplants, an innovative British band with an eclectic style. In the 1980s he played in Loose Tubes, as did Tim Garland (of 'Sister Moon') and Tim Whitehead ('All Is Well'). This simple folksy ballad in 3/4 contains some colourful shifts of key.
RELATED LISTENING Perfect Houseplants: 'Going Home' from *Perfect Houseplants* (Ah-Um)

# MOPTI
DON CHERRY
arr. Huw Warren

Notice
ABRSM has reluctantly had to remove this piece from this book since, despite many efforts, we have been unable to obtain permission from the copyright owner to reproduce it for this reprint.

blank page (see page 41)

blank page (see page 41)

ALL IS WELL
TIM WHITEHEAD

Straight 8s ♩ = 112 **Bright gospel**

Saxophonist Tim Whitehead (b. 1950) played in the seminal Loose Tubes band during the 1980s, before leading various other groups. His recent work explores links between jazz and contemporary classical music. This tune is influenced more by soul and gospel, where the spirit of the music is celebratory and outgoing.

RELATED LISTENING Tim Whitehead: *Personal Standards* (Home Made), and 'Come On Home' from *Silence Between Waves* (Ronnie Scott's Jazz House)

SARA'S TOUCH

MIKE MAINIERI
arr. Mike Hall

The New York vibe player and keyboardist Mike Mainieri (b. 1938) played in the fusion band Steps Ahead in the 1980s. The style 'fusion' developed in the late 1960s. It fused rock and Latin grooves and textures, and involved virtuosic improvisation.
RELATED LISTENING Steps Ahead: 'Sara's Touch' from *Smokin' in the Pit* (Better Days)

AUTUMN LEAVES

JOSEPH KOSMA & JOHNNY MERCER
arr. Nikki Iles

The essential jazz standard, 'Autumn Leaves' is to be found on page one of many jazz textbooks – it works well in a range of styles and has been interpreted by all the great improvisers, from Django Reinhardt to Miles Davis. Its chord sequence in the original is based around two key centres: G minor (in concert pitch) and its relative major, B♭. The arrangement here reflects Bill Evans's interpretation rather than Cannonball's.

RELATED LISTENING Cannonball Adderley: 'Autumn Leaves' from *Somethin' Else* (Blue Note)
Bill Evans: 'Autumn Leaves' from *Portrait in Jazz* (Original Jazz Classics)

LADY BE GOOD

GEORGE & IRA GERSHWIN
arr. Nikki Iles

George Gershwin (1898–1937) was a celebrated American songwriter, pianist and composer of concert music (including the famous *Rhapsody in Blue*). The true title of this song is in fact 'Oh, Lady, Be Good!', but this is normally shortened, as above. The song became the setting for a very famous sax solo recorded by Lester Young, in 1936.

RELATED LISTENING 'Lady Be Good' from *Jazz at the Philharmonic* (Arpeggio)
Lester Young: Title track from *Lady Be Good* (BCD)
Ella Fitzgerald: Title track from *Oh, Lady, Be Good!* (Verve)

SISTER MOON — TIM GARLAND

Composed by English saxophonist Tim Garland (b. 1966), 'Sister Moon' is lyrical and nocturnal, but it is not a ballad. Nor is it strictly speaking a bossa nova, despite the steady offbeats and the rhythm of the accompaniment. The rhythm found here is typical of some Brazilian music, particularly that of Egberto Gismonti.

RELATED LISTENING Tim Garland: 'The Moon for Her' from *Made by Walking* (Stretch)

GOING HOME

MARK LOCKHEART
arr. Pete Churchill

Saxophonist Mark Lockheart (b. 1961) plays in Perfect Houseplants, an innovative British band with an eclectic style. In the 1980s he played in Loose Tubes, as did Tim Garland (of 'Sister Moon') and Tim Whitehead ('All Is Well'). This simple folksy ballad in 3/4 contains some colourful shifts of key.

RELATED LISTENING Perfect Houseplants: 'Going Home' from *Perfect Houseplants* (Ah-Um)

18

 **DON CHERRY**
arr. Huw Warren

Notice
ABRSM has reluctantly removed this piece from this book.
Despite many efforts, we have been unable to obtain permission
from the copyright owner to reproduce it for reprint.

ALL IS WELL TIM WHITEHEAD

Saxophonist Tim Whitehead (b. 1950) played in the seminal Loose Tubes band during the 1980s, before leading various other groups. His recent work explores links between jazz and contemporary classical music. This tune is influenced more by soul and gospel, where the spirit of the music is celebratory and outgoing.

RELATED LISTENING Tim Whitehead: *Personal Standards* (Home Made), and 'Come On Home' from *Silence Between Waves* (Ronnie Scott's Jazz House)

20

SARA'S TOUCH

MIKE MAINIERI
arr. Mike Hall

The New York vibe player and keyboardist Mike Mainieri (b. 1938) played in the fusion band Steps Ahead in the 1980s. The style 'fusion' developed in the late 1960s. It fused rock and Latin grooves and textures, and involved virtuosic improvisation.
RELATED LISTENING Steps Ahead: 'Sara's Touch' from *Smokin' in the Pit* (Better Days)

PLAYING THE TUNES IN AN EXAM

In the exam you are required to perform three tunes from this book, one from each list. You will also have to do a number of supporting tests, which measure your technical proficiency, musicianship and ability to improvise. For full details of the exam, please refer to the Jazz Syllabus, which is available free of charge from music retailers, our website (www.abrsm.org) or from ABRSM, 24 Portland Place, London W1B 1LU, United Kingdom.

PREPARING THE TUNES

Jazz is an aural tradition, and we expect that you will learn the tunes from the CD as well as from the printed music. For the exam, the tunes do not have to be played exactly as written, and in fact embellishment of the HEAD (as distinct from improvisation in the SOLOS section) is expected, particularly after the SOLOS section.

In the exam the following elements of the given material must be in place:

- *the correct feel* – 'straight 8s' or 'swing', as and where marked.

- *the minimum speed.* The tempo marking, representing the minimum speed, should be observed in order to demonstrate the technical control required at the Level/Grade. You may prefer to play the tune faster and this is equally acceptable.

- *the melody of the HEAD.* This may be embellished – indeed, examiners will expect some embellishment on the return of the HEAD – but it must be recognizable. Your interpretation should demonstrate an understanding of the HEAD's main musical elements, such as important kicks, other rhythmic figures and the melody's contours, and of the musical character of the arrangement.

- *the routine*, that is the form of the arrangement, with the intro (where applicable), HEAD and SOLOS containing the correct number of bars. The length of solo for the exam is indicated at the end of SOLOS, in both score and part. (Many tunes contain repeat signs around the SOLOS section, to enable you to play longer solos in non-exam performances.)

- *the improvisation.* In Level/ Grade 1–3 exams the rhythmic and melodic aspects of your improvisation (in the SOLOS section) are assessed. At these early stages we expect your understanding of the relationship between melody and harmony to be developing gradually, as part of your playing, but this will not be assessed in the exam. Taking some account of the harmonic context in your solo will be given credit at Level/Grade 4 Distinction and above.

EMBELLISHING AND IMPROVISING

The process of interpreting and personalizing the tune begins once the given material is secure.

Playing the HEAD

On the first playing, the notation of the HEAD should be closely followed. While there may be variation in details of melody, rhythm or phrasing, the result should be coherent, stylish and musical, and not alter the technical level. The amount and nature of embellishment will vary from tune to tune, depending on its style and musical character.

Occasionally the HEAD contains melody notes printed in small type, accompanied by the abbreviation 'opt.' (optional). This means either that there are two commonly known versions of the tune or that it has been necessary to alter the melody slightly to suit the Level/Grade. Playing these optional notes is not a requirement of the exam, nor will they be assessed as if part of the written HEAD. However, if you prefer to include these small-type notes in the exam, you may, particularly where they form part of an embellishment.

Soloing and using guideline pitches

The guideline pitches provide a starting point for your solo. They reflect the number and range of pitches an examiner might expect to hear, and they take account of the scale requirements of the Level/Grade.

Please note that while you may use the pitches as a foundation for your solo, you will not be assessed in the exam on whether or not the guideline pitches are actually used. You will be expected to expand upon the given material as your experience allows. As your playing develops, the chords will increasingly influence the pitches you choose.

Preparing to improvise

Aim at improvising your solos and embellishing the given material at the moment of performance. Pre-prepared solos often lack the freshness, spontaneity and spirit of risk-taking that are at the heart of jazz. However, you are strongly advised to get to know the chord sequences and grooves of the tunes you have selected, and to learn as many ways through them as possible. You will then be able to demonstrate your skills in the exam through varying the musical material.

After the solo

The SOLOS section is usually followed by 'HEAD continues': the section in which the opening melody returns. Everything here may be embellished in any number of ways, from a few simple additions or variations to a more extensive reworking. As a guide, embellishment at Level/Grade 1 can mean small changes to the rhythm or melody, or variation in dynamics and phrasing. At Level/Grade 3, players might transpose material at the octave, or introduce fills. Finally, by Level/Grade 5, melodic lines may be developed with greater intricacy, and rhythms and phrasing reinterpreted. In short, exact repetition of earlier material should be avoided.

The performances on the CD demonstrate this approach, providing good examples of improvisations and embellishments of the given material. However, be inventive! Remember that examiners will be familiar with the CD and will notice slavish copying.

ACCOMPANIMENT

All the tunes must be played with an accompaniment. The options are:

- *minus-one backing-tracks*. The CD with this book includes a rhythm-section backing-track for each tune. In the exam these tracks are to be played on a portable CD player provided by the candidate. A tuning note is included on the CD.

- *written-out and improvised accompaniments*. Pianists may play from the fully written-out scores supplied with this book. Alternatively, the accompaniment may be improvised by a pianist, guitarist or other chordal accompanist, based on the written-out score, its chord symbols or a combination of the two.

- *small-band accompaniment*. Candidates may use a small band, provided the chord symbols and routines in this book are followed.

For further details, please refer to the Jazz Syllabus.

CD TRACK LISTING

TUNES

Performance/Minus-one

Blues & Roots

1	17	**BLUE TRAIN** John Coltrane arr. Liam Noble (*EMI United Partnership Ltd*)
2	18	**PLAYING IN THE YARD** Sonny Rollins arr. Pete Whittaker (*Sony/ATV Music Publishing (UK) Ltd*)
3	19	**ALL BLUES** Miles Davis arr. Nikki Iles (*Universal/MCA Music Ltd*)
4	20	**COLD DUCK TIME** Eddie Harris arr. Iain Dixon (*Sony/ATV Music Publishing (UK) Ltd*)
5	21	**THE PREACHER** Horace Silver arr. Liam Noble (*Universal Music Publishing MGB Ltd*)

Standards

6	22	**MERCY, MERCY, MERCY** Joe Zawinul arr. Phil Peskett (*Keith Prowse Music Publishing Co. Ltd*)
7	23	**HONEYSUCKLE ROSE** Thomas 'Fats' Waller & Andy Razaf arr. Nick Tomalin (*Redwood Music Ltd/Memory Lane Music Ltd*)
8	24	**TEA FOR TWO** Vincent Youmans & Irving Caesar arr. Bill Kinghorn (*Warner Chappell Music Ltd/Chappell Music Ltd*)
9	25	**AUTUMN LEAVES** Joseph Kosma & Johnny Mercer arr. Nikki Iles (*SACEM/Peter Maurice Music Co. Ltd*)
10	26	**LADY BE GOOD** George & Ira Gershwin arr. Nikki Iles (*Warner/Chappell North America Ltd*)

Contemporary Jazz

11	27	**SISTER MOON** Tim Garland (*ABRSM*)
12	28	**GOING HOME** Mark Lockheart arr. Pete Churchill (*Mark Lockheart*)
13	29	**MOPTI** Don Cherry arr. Huw Warren (*Notting Hill Music (UK) Ltd*)
14	30	**ALL IS WELL** Tim Whitehead (*ABRSM*)
15	31	**SARA'S TOUCH** Mike Mainieri arr. Mike Hall (*Redeye Music Publishing Co.*)
16		**TUNING NOTE** concert B♭

AURAL TESTS

32	**Test A, No. 1**
33	**Test B, No. 5**
34	**Test C, No. 1**

QUICK STUDIES

35	**No. 3** by ear
36	**No. 3** at sight

SCALES

37	**Lydian on D, 2 octaves** straight 8s
38	**B♭ major, 1 octave** swing
39	**Minor pentatonic on E, 1 octave** straight 8s
40	**Blues scale on A, 1 octave** swing
41	**Chromatic on G, 1 octave** swing
42	**C major arpeggio, 2 octaves** swing
43	**G minor arpeggio, 1 octave** straight 8s

Saxes: Alan Barnes, Steve Buckley, Ben Castle, Martin Hathaway, Mark Lockheart, Andy Panayi, Stan Sulzmann, Rob Townsend
Keyboards: Robin Aspland, Charles Beale, Pete Churchill, Nikki Iles, Liam Noble, Huw Warren, Jim Watson, Gareth Williams
Bass: Jeremy Brown, Orlando Le Fleming, Matt Miles, Dudley Phillips, Robert Rickenberg, Steve Watts
Drums/Percussion: Paul Clarvis, Mark Fletcher, Martin France, Nic France, Sebastiaan de Krom, Tristan Mailliot, Clark Tracey
Examiner: Charles Beale **Exam 'Candidates':** John Hayward, Nathan Hayward, Stan Sulzmann
Producers: Chris Batchelor, Charles Beale, Hywel Davies, Nikki Iles
Recording Engineer: Ken Blair
Assistant Recording Engineers: Jeremy Gill (Roundhouse), Gavin Goldberg (Metropolis), James Shannon (Surrey)

Recorded at The Roundhouse Studios, London, 25 March to 17 April and 24 June to 13 July 2002, Metropolis Studios Limited, London, 8 and 9 November 2002, and University of Surrey Studios, Guildford, 6 January 2003

A bmp production for ABRSM (Publishing) Ltd, a wholly owned subsidiary of ABRSM